W9-CHA-696

Weekly Reader books present

# An Animal for Alan

by Edward R. Ricciuti

Pictures by Tom Eaton

A Science I CAN READ Book

Harper & Row, Publishers
New York, Evanston, and London

Weekly Reader Books presents

# An Animal for Alan

by Edward R. Ricciuti

Pictures by Tom Eaton

A Science I CAN READ Book

Harper & Row, Publishers
New York, Evanston, and London

This book is a presentation of Weekly Reader Books.
Weekly Reader Books offers book clubs for children from
preschool through junior high school.

For further information write to:
**Weekly Reader Books**
1250 Fairwood Ave.
Columbus, Ohio 43216

AN ANIMAL FOR ALAN
Text copyright © 1970 by Edward Raphael Ricciuti
Pictures copyright © 1970 by Tom Eaton
All rights reserved. Printed in the United States of America. No part of this
book may be used or reproduced in any manner whatsoever without written
permission except in the case of brief quotations embodied in critical articles
and reviews. For information address Harper & Row, Publishers, Inc., 10 East
53rd Street, New York, N.Y. 10022. Published simultaneously in Canada by
Fitzhenry & Whiteside Limited, Toronto.
Library of Congress Catalog Card Number: 74-105460

For James Edward

"Look! A bird with a broken wing,"

Alan said to his father.

The bird called out

across the field.

It flopped around in the high grass.

"Let's catch that bird,"

said Alan.

"We can take it home for a pet."

"I bet you can't catch it,"

Alan's father said.

Alan ran into the high grass.

The bird fluttered away from him.

It went into some bushes

by a stream.

Alan ran after it.

"I have it!" he yelled.

He grabbed at the bird,

but it flew away.

"Kill-dee, kill-dee," the bird cried.

Alan saw a white stripe

on each of its brown wings.

"Kill-dee, kill-dee," it called.

"That bird sure got better fast,"

said Alan.

"It was not really hurt,"

said his father. "It fooled you.

There are probably baby birds

in the grass.

It led you away from its babies

by acting hurt.

That is how it tries

to protect its young,"

said his father.

"The bird is a killdeer.

It lives in fields and pastures."

"Kill-dee, kill-dee!" cried Alan.

He ran across the field,

flapping his arms.

Alan and his father

were on a hike.

They came to a pool in the brook.

Alan dipped his stick

into the water.

A small trout swam away.

Alan and his father

climbed over an old stone wall.

Then they were in the woods.

A chipmunk ran across their path

and into the bushes.

Alan ran after it.

Carefully he moved

the branches aside.

He could not believe what he saw.

A tiny fawn lay on the ground.

It was so close to Alan

that he could almost touch it.

The fawn had big dark eyes.

Its brown coat

was spotted with white.

The spots looked like the sunlight

on the leaves.

The fawn kept very still.

14

"Don't touch it,"

Alan's father said softly.

"It is only a few days old."

"Let's take it home," said Alan.

"That would not be good

for the fawn," said his father.

"Its home is here,

in the woods."

They quietly stepped away.

"I wish the fawn

could live with us," said Alan.

"A fawn is a wild animal,"

said his father.

"Most wild animals

are not good pets."

"But it was lost," said Alan.

"No," said his father.

"It was hiding.

When a fawn is very young,

it hides while its mother eats.

The fawn is safe because

other animals cannot smell it.

When the mother deer comes back,

the fawn will nurse."

Alan's father explained

that a fawn needs its mother's milk.

Milk from other animals is not

just right for a fawn.

That is why the fawn

should stay with its mother.

"Hungry?" asked Alan's father.

Alan had been waiting all morning

to eat his jelly sandwich

and hard-boiled egg.

They sat down on an old cedar log

and ate.

After lunch

Alan picked up the wrappings.

He put them in his pack.

As he walked,

Alan thought about

killdeer and fawns.

He wanted a pet.

Soon they were back at the brook

where the killdeer lived.

Sure enough, a killdeer flew by.

"Kill-dee, kill-dee," it cried.

It hopped around

in the grass.

It flapped its wings.

But this time it did not fool Alan.

He saw another killdeer.

It kept its head down

and ran through the grass.

With it were two tiny fluffy chicks.

They were young killdeer.

The young ones hid in the grass.

Now both big birds

tried to fool Alan and his father.

But they looked hard

in the grass and old leaves.

They found the two little killdeer.

The young birds lay flat

among the old leaves.

They stayed very still,

just like the fawn.

"You could walk right by

and not see them," Alan said.

The two big birds flew

into the grass.

"The little birds crawl

under the big birds

to keep warm," his father said.

On the way home

Alan told his father about a monkey.

He had seen it in a pet shop.

"I can't have a killdeer.

I can't have a fawn.

Can I have a monkey for a pet?"

asked Alan.

"Monkeys are not good pets,"
said his father.

"Why?" asked Alan.

"That is a hard question
to answer," said his father.

"But when you see
a bunch of monkeys
living together,
you will understand."

"Where can I see
a bunch of monkeys?"
asked Alan.

"At the zoo," said his father.

"I know a man who works there.

His name is Mr. Fisher.

I will take you

to see him tomorrow."

The next day they went to the zoo.

First, Mr. Fisher took Alan

to a cage full of little monkeys.

They jumped around so quickly

Alan could not count them.

28

One monkey, with big pink ears,

sat on a branch.

He stuffed an orange into his mouth

with both hands.

Then he threw the peel

onto the floor.

Alan saw orange peels

all over the floor.

A baby monkey sat on a branch,
close to its mother.

The baby was nursing.

The mother monkey looked at Alan
and put her arm around her baby.

The monkeys in the next cage

were even smaller.

The father, mother,

and the two tiny babies

had faces as white as snow.

Long black hair

grew around their faces.

Their tails were long and bushy.

31

The little monkeys bunched together.

Each time Alan moved,

the monkeys watched him.

"In most monkey families,"

said Mr. Fisher,

"the mothers take care of the young.

But in this kind of monkey family

the father helps too."

One of the babies hopped

onto its father's back.

It buried itself

in the father's long fur.

Its long tail curled up in the air.

Alan laughed.

"Now the father looks like

he has two tails," he said.

Alan watched the little monkeys
for a while.

"Would one of these little monkeys
make a good pet?"
he asked Mr. Fisher.

"It would be very hard
for you and for the monkey,"
said Mr. Fisher.

"Monkeys need each other
just like people need each other.
It is not good for a monkey
to be without other monkeys.

And did you notice

the smell in here?"

Alan wrinkled his nose.

"Yes," he said. "I sure did."

"Well," said Mr. Fisher,

"that is how your house would smell.

These little monkeys

must be kept warm.

They have to stay indoors."

Alan thought

about the pile of orange peels

and about the smell.

"I don't think my mother

would like a monkey in the house,"

he said.

"Are there any monkeys

you can keep out-of-doors?"

"Yes. Let's go look

at the zoo's Monkey Island,"

said Mr. Fisher.

"It was built for the big monkeys

that can live outdoors."

The island was covered with monkeys.

Monkeys sat on top of the rocks.

They ran up and down the rocks.

They popped out of holes

in the rocks.

Alan watched a young monkey get

a piece of lettuce

from the water.

A big old monkey walked over.

The young one yelped

at the big one.

The big one jumped at him,

and the young one fell

into the water.

Two young monkeys chased

each other up a tree

and out onto a branch.

Then they began to wrestle.

A big monkey walked over

to pick up an apple.

The other monkeys moved away.

"That one is the boss

of all the monkeys on the island,"

said Mr. Fisher.

"What big teeth," said Alan.

"He bites too," said Mr. Fisher.

The monkey opened its mouth wide.

"He would not be a good pet either,"

said Alan.

Mr. Fisher took Alan to meet

the zoo nurse.

She had a young raccoon

on her shoulder.

"Is that your pet?" asked Alan.

"I am taking care of him,"

the nurse said,

"because his mother is sick."

"That must be fun," said Alan.

"Yes," said the nurse,

"but he gets into a lot of trouble."

The raccoon ran

down the nurse's arm.

"Oops!" she said.

"He just tore my sweater."

The raccoon ran over to Alan

and climbed up his leg.

"Hey, he is trying to eat my shirt!"

said Alan.

The zoo nurse grabbed the raccoon

and put him on the floor.

"Now he has your paper clips,"

said Alan.

"You see," said the zoo nurse,

"I must watch him all the time.

At night I have to take him home,"

she told Alan.

"He pulls my hair

when I am sleeping

and wakes me up.

He does not like to be alone."

"Then I cannot have a raccoon

for a pet," said Alan.

"I go to school all day."

49

After that, Mr. Fisher showed Alan

a deer pasture.

It was bigger than Alan's yard—

even bigger than the school yard.

The fence around it was very high.

"Deer can jump higher than my head,"

said Mr. Fisher.

The spotted fawns made Alan think
of the one he saw in the woods.
They were nursing.

"Why don't all the deer have antlers?"
asked Alan.

"Only buck deer have antlers,"

said Mr. Fisher.

"What are buck deer?" asked Alan.

"They are the males,"

said Mr. Fisher.

"They shed their antlers once a year.

Now the bucks

are growing new antlers.

Antlers are very sharp,"

Mr. Fisher said.

"Sometimes bucks fight

with their antlers and hooves.

Even fawns have sharp hooves."

Alan looked at the deer.

"I guess they would not make

such good pets," he said.

"Zoo animals are not really pets,"

said Mr. Fisher.

"Zoo men work hard

to care for their wild animals.

The animals must live in places

that are like their wild homes.

They need the right food."

"Are any wild animals

good for pets?" asked Alan.

"Sure," said Mr. Fisher,

"if you have the time

to care for them.

How about these hamsters?

Did you know that in the wild,

hamsters dig deep burrows?

And you could keep

this kind of salamander.

It needs an aquarium

with a rock, a plant,

and a little water.

Or maybe you would like

a tree frog, a king snake,

or a cricket."

"A cricket?" said Alan.

"Yes," said Mr. Fisher.

"In Japan, children keep them

in cages."

It had been a long day at the zoo.

Alan thanked Mr. Fisher

and left with his father.

"I think it is time

for you to have a pet,"

said Alan's father.

"And I know some animals

that might be just right.

Some are small.

Some are big.

They come in all colors

and shapes.

You can teach them tricks too."

"Those animals sound great,"

said Alan.

"What are they?"

His father laughed.

"Dogs and cats," he said.